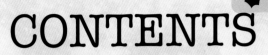

CONTENTS

EARLY MEDICINE

In ancient times illness was seen as the result of witchcraft or the will of the gods. Often, patients would pray and make offerings to a god. The rise of scientific medicine in the last two centuries has replaced these historical practices.

ANCIENT MEDICINE

Although little was known about the workings of the human body, early medicine provided some effective cures. Plants were being used as herbal medicines as early as 25,000 BC. Drilling teeth was practised over 5,000 years ago in India, while in ancient Egypt, the earliest known surgery was performed around 2750 BC. In ancient Greece, the first known medical school was set up in 700 BC. Later, Hippocrates founded a school in Kos, Greece, in around 400 BC. Hippocrates is called 'the father of medicine'. He and his followers were the first to describe many diseases and medical conditions.

Imhotep was the first known doctor. He lived in ancient Egypt over 4,500 years ago.

Hippocrates (460-370 BC)

MIDDLE AGES

After the fall of the Roman Empire, around AD 400, medical knowledge in Europe was based mainly on Greek and Roman writings. Ideas about diseases and cures were a mixture of ancient knowledge, spiritual beliefs and astrology! Understanding how the body worked through anatomical studies was held back by religious laws. It wasn't until the 16th century that anatomy studies were revived and important discoveries were made about the human body. Despite the religious views, anatomy schools sprang up in universities all around Europe. By the middle of the 19th century the anatomy of the human body was available to doctors as the printed *Gray's Anatomy*.

GRAPHIC DISCOVERIES

MEDICAL BREAKTHROUGHS

by Gary Jeffrey

illustrated by Terry Riley

W
FRANKLIN WATTS
LONDON•SYDNEY

First published in 2009 by Franklin Watts

Franklin Watts
338 Euston Road
London NW1 3BH

Franklin Watts Australia
Level 17/207 Kent Street
Sydney, NSW 2000

A CIP catalogue record for this book is available from the British Library.

Dewey number: 610.9

ISBN: 978 0 7496 9240 7

Franklin Watts is a division of Hachette Children's Books, an Hachette UK company.
www.hachette.co.uk

GRAPHIC DISCOVERIES: MEDICAL BREAKTHROUGHS produced for Franklin
Watts by David West Children's Books, 7 Princeton Court, 55 Felsham Road,
London SW15 1AZ

Designed and produced by
David West Children's Books

Editor: Gail Bushnell

Photo credits:
4b, National Library of Medicine; 6b, Library of Congress Prints and Photographs
Division Washington, D.C.; 7tr, Corbis; 7tl, Public Health Image Library; 44tl&r,
Corbis.

Printed in China

Website disclaimer:
Note to parents and teachers: Every effort has been made by the Publishers to ensure
that the websites in this book are suitable for children, that they are of the highest
educational value, and that they contain no inappropriate or offensive material.
However, because of the nature of the Internet, it is impossible to guarantee that the
contents of these sites will not be altered. We strongly advise that the Internet is
supervised by a responsible adult.

Leonardo da Vinci (1452-1519) was a brilliant artist and anatomist, among many other things, and made anatomical drawings (right). One of these inspired a British heart surgeon to find a new way to repair damaged hearts in 2005.

The study of anatomy flourished in the 17th and 18th centuries, as seen in this typical scene, Anatomy Lesson of Dr Nicolaes Tulp, by Rembrandt van Rijn, 1632 (below).

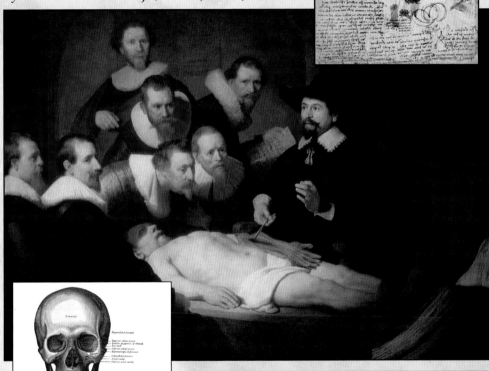

Even when using Gray's Anatomy (above), doctors of the 18th and 19th centuries were often ignorant about the human body. They gave cure-all potions and bled patients, which often did more harm than good, as illustrated in William Hogarth's The Visit to the Doctor, 1743 (right).

A BRIEF HISTORY OF MEDICAL SCIENCE

The search to understand how the human body works has taken many centuries. Along the way, medical inventions and discoveries have improved our understanding and our ability to treat illnesses and infections.

A scholar with glasses in Das Narrenschiff *(1494).*

INVENTIONS AND DISCOVERIES

• **Artificial limbs** have been around since ancient times. Around 500 BC, Herodotus wrote of a prisoner who escaped his chains by cutting off his foot, which he replaced later with a wooden one. In 1529, French surgeon Ambroise Paré used amputation to save lives. Soon after, he started developing artificial limbs.

• **Glasses** first appeared in common use during the late 13th century. Marco Polo first reported seeing them in China in 1275.

• **Vaccination** was discovered by the English doctor Edward Jenner, who successfully immunised a young boy against smallpox in 1796. Louis Pasteur, a French chemist, confirmed that germs cause disease and invented **pasteurisation** to kill germs in liquids in 1862. He also created the first vaccine for rabies.

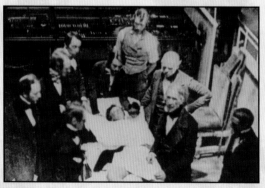

Reenactment of the first operation under anaesthesia (ether) by W. Morton.

• **Anaesthetics** were used in a crude form by the Incas, who caused numbness by chewing coca leaves and spitting the mixture into the wound they were operating on. Nitrous oxide (laughing gas) was used in the 1790s on a small scale, usually by dentists. In 1846, an American dentist performed the first public showing of a new anaesthetic called ether. Chloroform was also used at this time, but many patients died if it was not given properly.

- **Antiseptics,** substances that prevent infection, were first introduced to modern surgery by an English surgeon, Joseph Lister, in 1867. He used carbolic acid to clean wounds and surgical instruments.
- **X-rays** were discovered by the German scientist Wilhelm Roentgen in 1895. He realised their medical use when he made an image of his wife's hand using X-rays.

A medical X-ray reveals the unseen.

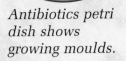

Antibiotics petri dish shows growing moulds.

- **Antibiotics,** derived from moulds and plants, were used by many ancient civilisations to treat infections. Modern antibiotic use began with the discovery of penicillin in 1928, by Scottish biologist Alexander Fleming. During World War II, many thousands of lives were saved by penicillin preventing infection of wounds.
- The structure of **DNA**, the molecule that carries our genetic information, was discovered by Crick and Watson in 1953.
- In 1957, an American engineer, Earl Bakken, made the first wearable, external **artificial heart pacemaker**. It had controls to change the heart's pace and was connected through wires to the heart.

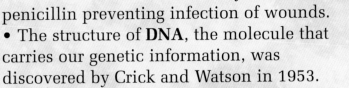

A heart pacemaker

- The first human **heart transplant** was successfully made by South African, Christiaan Barnard, in 1967.
- **The CAT scanner** can make 3D images of the inside of the human body. It was invented by an English engineer, Godfrey Hounsfield, and the first scans were made in 1971.

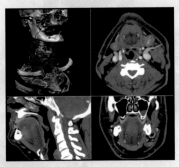

Images from a CAT scan.

- **Ultrasound scanning** uses sound to produce moving images of internal organs of the human body. One of its many uses is to check the growth of a baby inside a pregnant woman. It was refined from industrial ultrasound equipment by a Scottish doctor, Ian Donald, in 1958.

THE DISCOVERY OF DNA

IN 1859 BRITISH NATURALIST CHARLES DARWIN PUBLISHES 'THE ORIGIN OF SPECIES', IN WHICH HE SETS FORTH HIS THEORY OF EVOLUTION.

IN 1868 HE VISITS THE POET ALFRED LORD TENNYSON...

...SO, ALTHOUGH WE UNDERSTAND THE *THEORY* OF EVOLUTION, WE DON'T KNOW THE WORKINGS OF IT.

EXACTLY—*HOW* DO LIFE FORMS, LIKE THESE SWEET PEAS, CHANGE OVER MILLIONS OF YEARS?

WHOEVER UNCOVERS THE SECRET OF THE MECHANISM WILL HAVE SOLVED THE BIGGEST PUZZLE OF ALL!

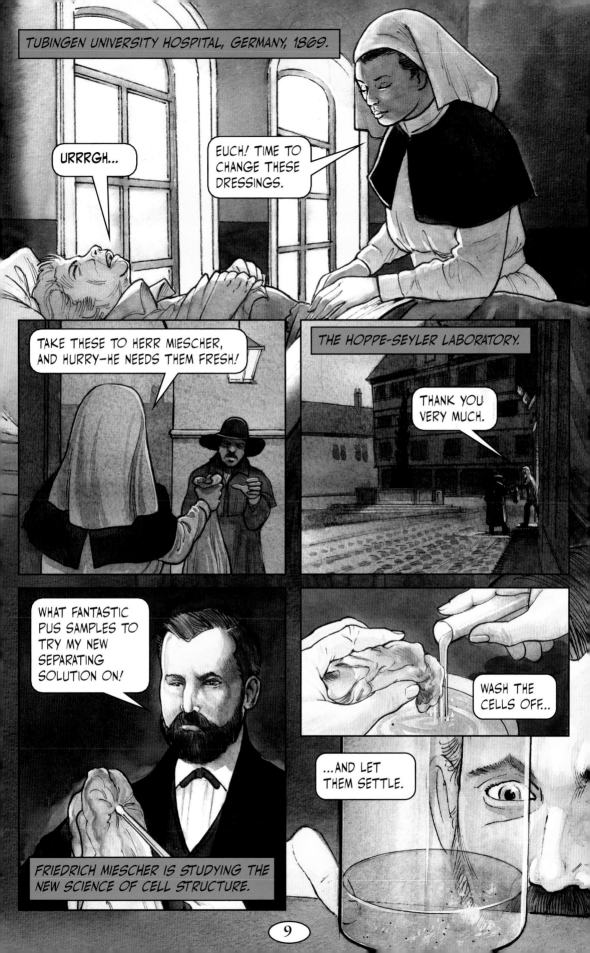

WE *DO* KNOW BACTERIA CAN MOVE GENETIC MATERIAL BETWEEN EACH OTHER WITHIN A LIQUID.

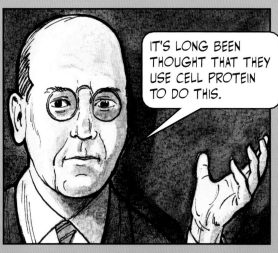

IT'S LONG BEEN THOUGHT THAT THEY USE CELL PROTEIN TO DO THIS.

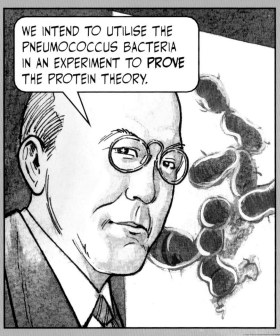

WE INTEND TO UTILISE THE PNEUMOCOCCUS BACTERIA IN AN EXPERIMENT TO **PROVE** THE PROTEIN THEORY.

PNEUMOCOCCUS **S** STRAIN CAUSES PNEUMONIA IN MICE, THE **R** STRAIN DOESN'T. MIXING THE **S** STRAIN WITH THE **R** STRAIN CAUSES THE **R** STRAIN TO BECOME DEADLY.

SO WHATEVER WE REMOVE FROM THE **S** STRAIN THAT STOPS IT FROM *TRANSFORMING* THE **R** STRAIN, THAT WILL BE THE **CARRIER** OF GENETIC MATERIAL.

LATER...

THE S STRAIN PROTEINS ARE ALL GONE? OKAY, MIX IT WITH THE **R** STRAIN AND INJECT IT.

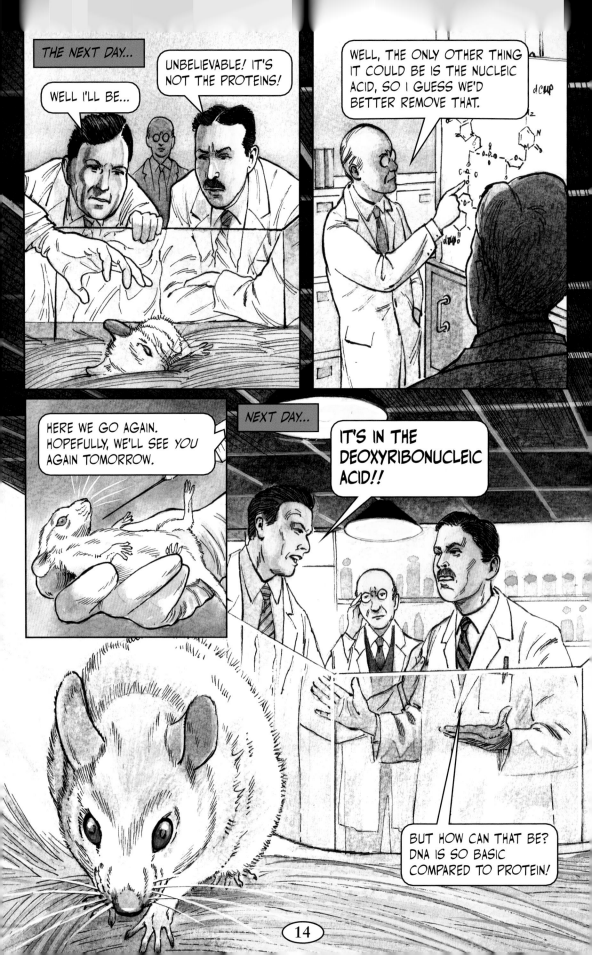

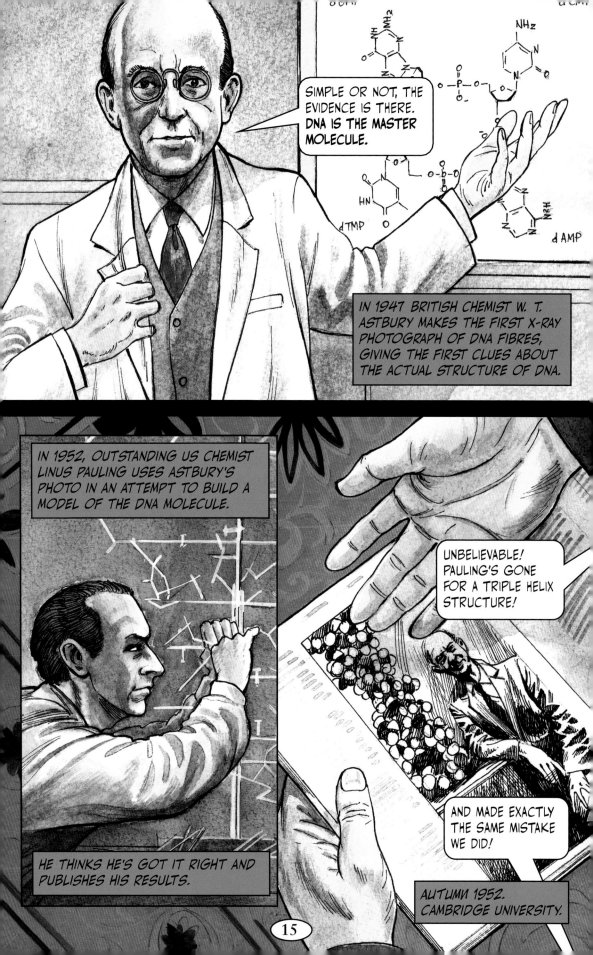

TWO RESEARCH STUDENTS, AMERICAN JAMES WATSON AND ENGLISHMAN FRANCIS CRICK, HAVE ALREADY FAILED WITH THEIR OWN FIRST MODEL-BUILDING ATTEMPT...

ALSO, I DON'T GET WHAT'S HOLDING HIS MOLECULE TOGETHER. I DON'T SEE AN ELECTRICAL CHARGE.

CORRECT. IN FACT, IT ISN'T EVEN AN ACID ANYMORE. HE'S IGNORED THE MOST BASIC RULES OF CHEMISTRY!

THIS IS SO WRONG THAT WE MUST HAVE ANOTHER TRY AT A MODEL.

HMM...IF ONLY WE HAD A BETTER PICTURE THAN THE ASTBURY PHOTO TO WORK FROM...

KINGS COLLEGE, LONDON...

ROSALIND, YOU'RE A GENIUS!

THIS WET FORM OF DNA* IS SO CLEAR!

ROSALIND FRANKLIN HAS BEEN TAKING X-RAY PHOTOGRAPHS OF MOLECULES.

*FRANKLIN CLEVERLY FIGURED OUT THAT DNA SUCKS UP A LOT OF WATER.

JAMES, I'VE GOT SOMETHING HERE YOU MIGHT WANT TO TAKE A LOOK AT.

OH, MY...IT'S GOT A DOUBLE HELIX STRUCTURE. IT'S AS PLAIN AS DAY!

MAURICE WILKINS IS STUDYING DNA ALONGSIDE FRANKLIN.

I WONDER IF PAULING HAS SEEN THIS?...NO, HE CAN'T HAVE!

ROSALIND'S STOPPING HER WORK ON DNA, YOU KNOW.

YOU'RE KIDDING!

NO, SHE'S MORE INTERESTED IN VIRUSES!

USING INFORMATION GATHERED FROM DIFFERENT SOURCES, WATSON AND CRICK WORKED TO PIECE THE PUZZLE TOGETHER...

SO IF GUANINE PAIRS WITH CYTOSINE, THEN ADENINE MUST PAIR WITH THYMINE. I'VE DONE IT!

IT'S SELF-COPYING!

IN 1962, CRICK AND WATSON, ALONG WITH MAURICE WILKINS, ARE AWARDED THE NOBEL PRIZE FOR MEDICINE.

SADLY, ROSALIND FRANKLIN DIED IN 1958 BEFORE SHE COULD BE ACKNOWLEDGED FOR HER CONTRIBUTION.

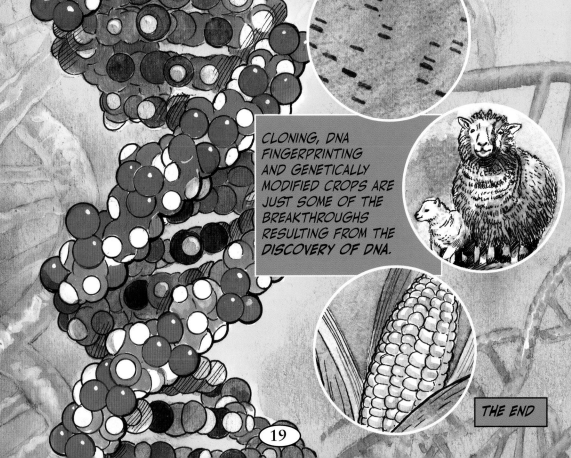

THE SCIENCE OF MOLECULAR GENETICS HAS CHANGED THE WORLD.

CLONING, DNA FINGERPRINTING AND GENETICALLY MODIFIED CROPS ARE JUST SOME OF THE BREAKTHROUGHS RESULTING FROM THE DISCOVERY OF DNA.

THE END

THE FIRST HEART TRANSPLANT

GROOTE SCHUUR HOSPITAL, CAPE TOWN, SOUTH AFRICA, 1966...

THIS NEW HEART-LUNG MACHINE IS A LOT QUIETER THAN THE OLD ONE.

IT'S ALSO DESIGNED TO CAUSE LESS DAMAGE TO THE PATIENT'S BLOOD SUPPLY.

THAT WILL SURELY HELP...

MR NAKI!

DR BARNARD, THE NEW HEART IS **READY**.

CHRISTIAAN BARNARD IS A TOP HEART SURGEON.

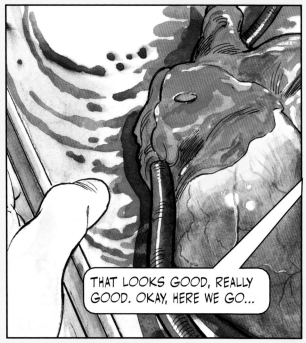

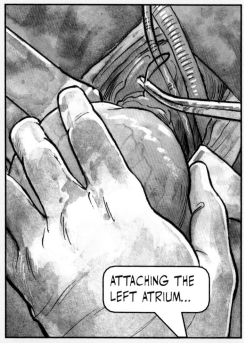

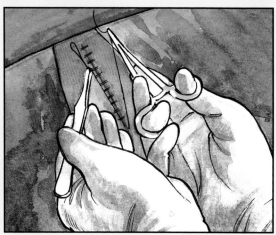

21

THREE DAYS LATER...

THE PATIENT IS DOING WELL!

TERRIFIC!

THINK YOU'RE READY TO TRY THIS ON A HUMAN?

YES, I DO. ALL I NEED ARE THE RIGHT PATIENTS TO SHOW UP...

BANG!

CAR ACCIDENT VICTIM - NAME'S DENISE DARVALL.

3 DECEMBER 1967, EMERGENCY ROOM, GROOTE SCHUUR...

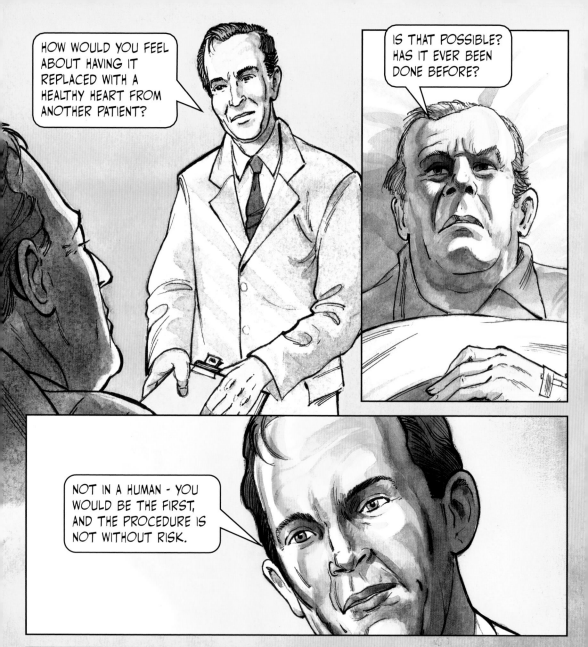

HOW WOULD YOU FEEL ABOUT HAVING IT REPLACED WITH A HEALTHY HEART FROM ANOTHER PATIENT?

IS THAT POSSIBLE? HAS IT EVER BEEN DONE BEFORE?

NOT IN A HUMAN - YOU WOULD BE THE FIRST, AND THE PROCEDURE IS NOT WITHOUT RISK.

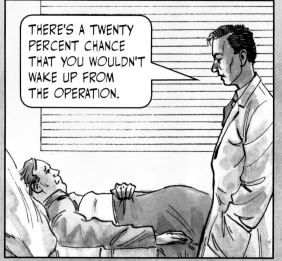

THERE'S A TWENTY PERCENT CHANCE THAT YOU WOULDN'T WAKE UP FROM THE OPERATION.

TAKE A COUPLE OF DAYS TO THINK ABOUT IT.

9:00 PM...

BWEEEEEEEEEEEEEEEBEEEEEEE...

THAT'S IT, DENISE HAS FLATLINED!

WE NEED TO WORK FAST.

THE MACHINE IS READY.

CRAAARK!

CRACKING CHEST.

LINES ARE IN...

OXYGENATING!

CLAMPING...HEART IS ISOLATED.

FLOW-RATE SET TO LOW, DR BARNARD.

HOLY MOLY, IT'S GOING TO WORK!

6:25 AM...

OKAY, IT'S TIME TO SWITCH OFF THE MACHINE.

BEEP-BEEP-BEEP...

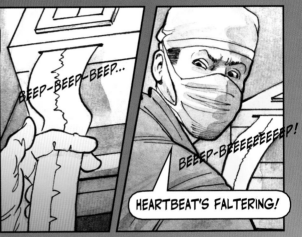

BEEEP-BREEEEEEEEP!

HEARTBEAT'S FALTERING!

RECONNECT IT!

FIVE MINUTES LATER, THE MACHINE IS SUCCESSFULLY DISCONNECTED.

THE ENTIRE PROCEDURE HAS TAKEN JUST OVER FOUR HOURS.

THAT'S IT. THANK YOU, EVERYBODY, WE'RE DONE.

I NEED A CUP OF TEA!

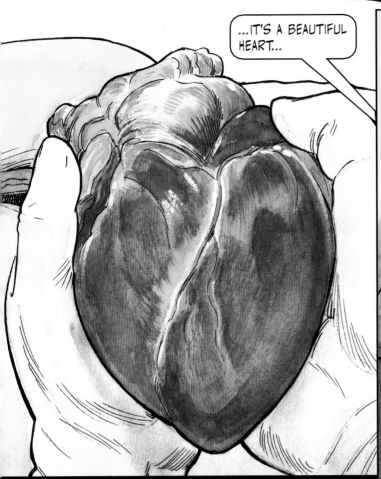

...IT'S A BEAUTIFUL HEART...

...THAT PUMPED STRONGLY RIGHT TO THE END.

WASHKANSKY HAD DIED BECAUSE OF HIS WEAKENED IMMUNE SYSTEM. HIS ACTUAL TRANSPLANT HAD BEEN A TOTAL SUCCESS.

ALTHOUGH BARNARD'S ACHIEVEMENT PAVED THE WAY FOR MORE HEART TRANSPLANTS, IT WASN'T UNTIL THE DISCOVERY OF NEW ANTI-REJECTION DRUGS THAT TRANSPLANTS BECAME MORE COMMONPLACE...AND RELIABLE.

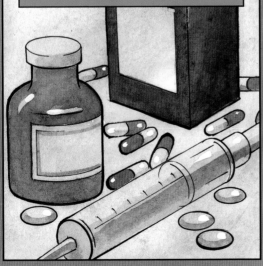

TO DATE, THE WORLD'S LONGEST-LIVING SINGLE HEART TRANSPLANTEE IS AMERICAN TONY HUESMAN.

HIS DONOR HEART HAS BEEN BEATING FOR MORE THAN 28 YEARS.

THE END

THE WORLD'S FIRST BIONIC WOMAN

ARKANSAS, 2004. US ARMY VETERAN CLAUDIA MITCHELL IS BEING TAKEN FOR A RIDE IN THE COUNTRY...

BBRMHAHHHHHH!

UH-OH, I THINK WE'RE COMING IN A LITTLE TOO FAST...

OH NO - WE'RE GOING TO...

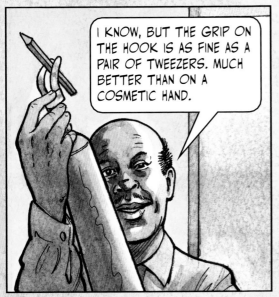

I KNOW, BUT THE GRIP ON THE HOOK IS AS FINE AS A PAIR OF TWEEZERS. MUCH BETTER THAN ON A COSMETIC HAND.

YEAH AND I MEAN, WHO AM I TRYING TO KID, RIGHT?

IT WILL TAKE QUITE A BIT OF PRACTICE...

LATER AT HOME...

OH, MAN! I JUST CAN'T WORK THIS THING!

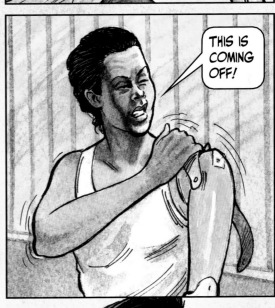

THIS IS COMING OFF!

I WANT TO PEEL A BANANA... WHAT AM I GOING TO DO?

THIS IS SO HUMILIATING...

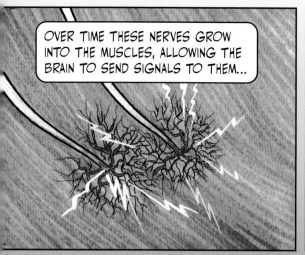

OVER TIME THESE NERVES GROW INTO THE MUSCLES, ALLOWING THE BRAIN TO SEND SIGNALS TO THEM...

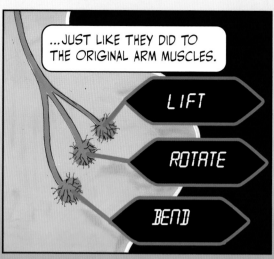

...JUST LIKE THEY DID TO THE ORIGINAL ARM MUSCLES.

LIFT

ROTATE

BEND

SENSORS IN THE COMPUTERISED ARM ARE HOOKED UP TO THE CHEST MUSCLES.

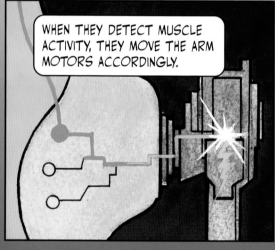

WHEN THEY DETECT MUSCLE ACTIVITY, THEY MOVE THE ARM MOTORS ACCORDINGLY.

SO JUST MY THOUGHTS WILL CONTROL THE ARM?

YES!

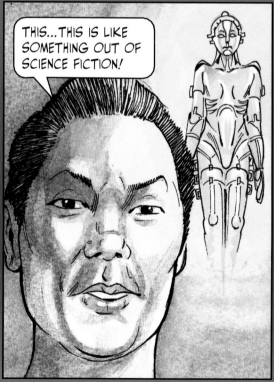

THIS...THIS IS LIKE SOMETHING OUT OF SCIENCE FICTION!

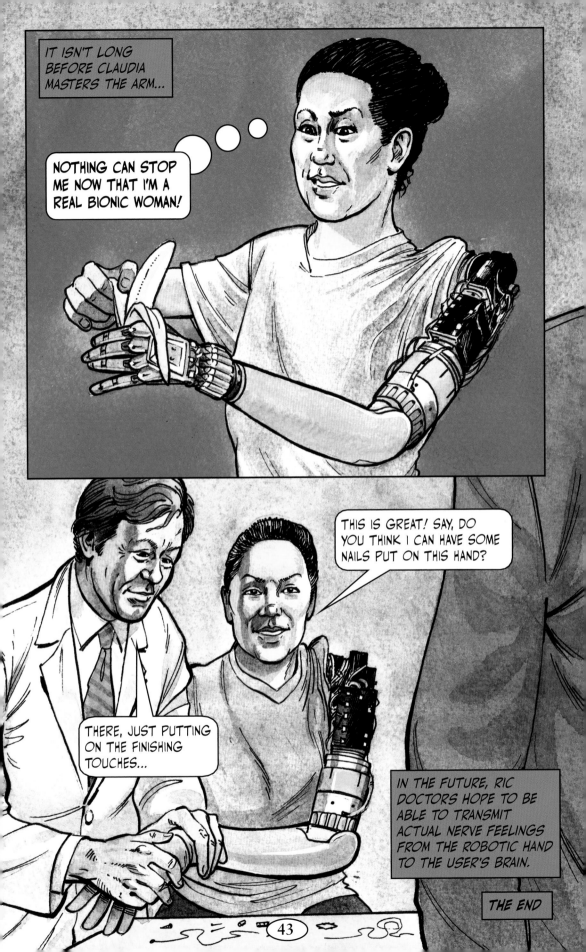

MEDICINE FOR THE 21ST CENTURY

Since the groundbreaking medical developments of the late 20th century, medicine has turned science fiction into fact, from bionic people to cloning.

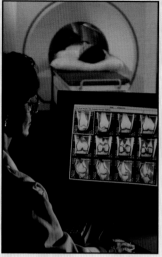

Computers play a major role in today's medicine. An MRI scanner linked to a computer uses radio frequency signals to see inside a patient.

DNA

The story of DNA has continued since its

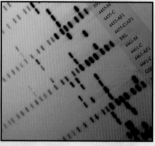

DNA 'blueprint' on film.

discovery. Today, criminals can be caught by forensic scientists using DNA blueprints to match samples left at a crime scene with those of the culprit.

DNA has also led to the understanding and prevention of genetic diseases. Drugs have been made from genetically-engineered organisms since the 1980s, using animals such as cows, goats and sheep as the 'factories'. In the future, scientists think they will 'grow' drugs in chicken eggs. A chicken can lay 330 eggs a year, so cheap drugs could be available to all.

CLONING

In 1996, a sheep named Dolly, was reproduced from a single cell, or 'cloned', meaning she had only one parent. Many disagree with the science of cloning, but it could help to preserve endangered species.

Dolly the sheep, the first cloned mammal, died in 2003.

PROSTHETICS

Except for the brain and nervous system, almost every part of our bodies can be replaced, from blood and veins to newly grown skin and electronic prosthetics (see right).

TRANSPLANTS

Surgeons today can repair the human body, not just to function but to return to a fully active life. The future holds much in store, with microchips for parts of the brain and to help blind people see. The list below shows what is already available.

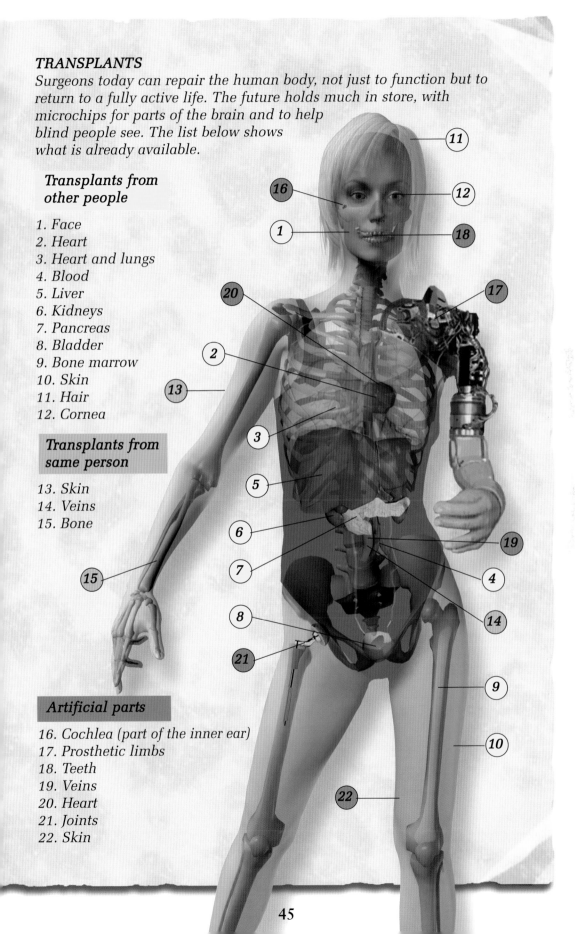

Transplants from other people

1. Face
2. Heart
3. Heart and lungs
4. Blood
5. Liver
6. Kidneys
7. Pancreas
8. Bladder
9. Bone marrow
10. Skin
11. Hair
12. Cornea

Transplants from same person

13. Skin
14. Veins
15. Bone

Artificial parts

16. Cochlea (part of the inner ear)
17. Prosthetic limbs
18. Teeth
19. Veins
20. Heart
21. Joints
22. Skin

GLOSSARY

amputation Cutting off a limb using surgery.

anatomy The science of studying the structure of humans and animals, often through cutting them open.

astrology Observing stars and planets and how they affect people.

autopsy Medical investigation of a body to find out the cause of death.

bacteriologist A person who studies bacteria - simple, living things that multiply and can cause disease.

cell The smallest unit of a living thing.

cytoplasm The material inside a cell other than the nucleus.

diabetes A medical disorder that affects the production of energy within human (or animal) cells.

elementary analysis Detailed examination of the structure of something.

evolution The way living things are thought to have developed from earlier forms.

faltering Losing strength.

gene Part of a chromosome that passes on hereditary information.

genetic Relating to genes or heredity.

graft Transplant surgically.

helix A three-dimensional shape like a spiral staircase.

heredity The passing on of characteristics from parent to offspring.

immune system The body's ability to protect itself against disease.

immunisation The process of programming (inoculating) the body to protect itself from certain diseases.

isolated Separated from.

ligament Structure that supports an organ and holds it in place.

molecule Smallest part of a chemical.

nucleotides Basic structural unit (the rungs in the ladder) of DNA.

nucleus Important part of a cell, which holds the genetic material.

oxygenating Enriching with oxygen.

pneumococcus Bacteria associated with pneumonia.

pneumonia Inflammation of a lung, caused by bacteria or a virus. Inflammation of both lungs is called double pneumonia.

protein A complicated family of molecules, important to our bodies.

pus A thick, yellowish liquid produced in infected body parts.

strains Different types of the same organism.

theories A set of ideas to explain something.

viruses Body invaders that multiply inside cells, causing disease.

white blood cells Blood cells that fight foreign matter and disease.

FOR MORE INFORMATION

ORGANISATIONS

The Thackray Museum
Beckett Street
Leeds LS9 7LN
0113 244 4343
E-mail: info@thackraymuseum.org
Website: www.thackraymuseum.org

The Science Museum
Exhibition Road
South Kensington
London SW7 2DD
0870 870 4868
E-mail: feedback@nmsi.ac.uk
Website: www.sciencemuseum.org.uk

FURTHER READING

Ballard, Carol. *Organ Transplantation* (Cutting Edge Medicine).
London: Franklin Watts, 2007.

de la Bedoyere, Camilla. *The Discovery of DNA* (Milestones in
Modern Science). London: Evans Publishing Group, 2005.

Campbell, Andrew. *Organ Transplantation* (Science in the News).
London: Franklin Watts, 2008.

Craft, Dr Naomi. *The Little Book of Medical Breakthroughs*. London:
New Holland Publishers Ltd, 2008.

Vaughn, Jenny. *Genetics* (Science in the News). London: Franklin
Watts, 2008.

Watson, James D. *The Double Helix: Personal Account of the
Discovery of the Structure of DNA* (Penguin Longman Readers).
London: Longman, 2001.

INDEX